WISE TALES FROM THE JEWISH WORLD

The Essential Collection

Uri Kaplan

Prapañca
Press

First Edition

Prapanca Press.

Prapanca_press@protonmail..com.

Library of Congress Cataloging-in-Publication Data

Names: Kaplan, Uri, author.
Title: Wise Tales From the Jewish World: The Essential Collection / Uri Kaplan.
Description: Prapanca Press, 2020. │Series: Wise Tales. Volume 2.
Identifiers: LCCN 2020917477 │ISBN 9789659285129 (hardcover) │ISBN 9789659285136 (softcover) │ ISBN 9789659285143 (e-book)
Subjects: Judaism—Sources of Jewish religion—Rabbinical literature │ Literature (general)—Literary history—Folk literature—Fables
Classification: BM495-532 │ PN980-9

WISE TALES FROM THE JEWISH WORLD

How many pens are broken,

How many ink bottles are consumed,

To write about things that have never occurred!

Midrash Tanhuma

Some say stories put people to sleep,

But I say stories wake people up from their slumber!

Rabbi Nachman of Breslov

Table of Contents

Foreword

MANY YEARS AGO, Truth was roaming the streets completely naked. Anyone who saw him averted their eyes in embarrassment or hurried away in fear. Mothers would grab their children's hands and pull them away. Truth was unable to touch a single soul. He was lonely and hopeless.

All this changed when one day Truth unexpectedly came across Parable. Parable was strolling elegantly in a park, dressed in beautiful clothes. The sight of the naked Truth did not faze him. He observed Truth sympathetically and asked: "Why do you look so miserable?"

"It is because no one likes me," explained Truth. "Everyone tries to avoid me."

Parable pitied the naked Truth. "Let me help you," he offered. "The secret is that people are usually attracted to beautiful things. They also like things that are a bit disguised. Let me lend you some of my exquisite clothing, and you will see that people will love you!"

Truth was a little reluctant at first, but he soon decided to give it a shot. He put on Parable's attractive clothes, and sure enough, the new attire fit Truth perfectly. Tastefully dressed, he gradually earned the people's respect and appreciation. Ever since that day, Truth and Parable have walked hand in hand, and everyone admired them both.

This remarkable parable about parables was written by Jewish storyteller Ya'akov Krants in the eighteenth century. Yet, the allure of charming parables dressing up the truth conveys an everlasting reality. Buddha called it *upaya*, or "skillful means", and Jesus—as is well known—made extensive use of parables in his teachings. The Jewish tradition refers to such fables and parables as *Aggadah*, literally meaning "a telling", but also conveying the concept of a fairytale. For fairytales often disguise the naked truth.

HaBa'al Shem Tov, the charismatic founder of the Jewish Hassidic Movement, linked stories to chariots, which can lead people directly to the secrets of God. Esoteric Kabbalistic Jews spoke of the healing powers of stories and viewed "the telling" as a mystical religious practice in and of itself. Some Jews considered the telling of stories to be a Mitzvah—a religious duty commanded by God. In the nineteenth century, Rabbi Israel Friedman believed that stories were even more important than prayer. Legend has it that he often skipped the evening prayers in order to tell his students the exemplary tales of the Jewish sages.

Contemporary Israeli poet, Pinchas Sadeh, once mused that for religious people life is an allegory of God, while for psychologists God is the allegory of life. Whether we like it or not, we may be living inside the guts of leviathan parables, comprehending our lives and our gods via "a telling"—through fables that provide both meaning and hope.

The fifty-five short stories that follow were selected from numerous Jewish sources stretching back close to two millennia. Many were extracted from the early rabbinical literature of the Talmud and the Midrash, that were first put into writing in the early fifth century. Other tales belong to later literature transcribed in the Middle Ages. Some of the most engaging fables in this volume were borrowed from the Hassidic Movement of the eighteenth and nineteenth centuries.

The Jewish tradition contains thousands of fables and parables, and my aim has been to sift through the gravel and keep the gold. I rewrote the stories in simple prose and attempted to create a manageable collection of tales that could be enjoyed by any contemporary reader, not just by the scholarly or the pious. While Jews may find in the stories some of the wisdom of their ancestors, I believe the main themes of the book are universal and may inspire a much larger audience — an audience of teachers and parents, of students and counselors, of Christians, Buddhists, Hindus, Muslims, and non-religious people alike. Some of the tales carry with them a timeless message, one that could be appreciated by people anywhere and anytime simply due to their shared humanity.

Growing up in Israel, I heard many of these tales from teachers and relatives as a young boy. For that reason, I tended to view traditional *Aggadah* as simplistic moralistic tales aimed primarily for children. But revisiting these old parables today—some forty years later—has been a true revelation. I rediscovered deeper existential meanings in many of the fables and noticed surprising parallels with other folktales from around the world. I can only hope that readers will find these stories as engaging, thought-provoking, amusing, and powerful as I did.

I suggest reading the stories in this collection deliberately and leisurely, chewing them bit by bit, and possibly discussing them with others. That would indeed be the best way to digest the full flavor of every tale. For we must not forget that these stories are not only meant to teach, awaken, and remind us of forgotten truths, but also to amuse and entertain us. They are meant to be shared and debated in social settings. They are meant to help us reflect on our lives, but also to give us a respite from them. So, let us jump right in, and allow these tantalizing tales to work their charm.

The Long Spoons

RABBI CHAIM ELCHANAN spent much of his time searching for answers about the afterlife. He studied all available books but could not find a reliable description of Heaven and Hell. He visited all known sages, but they, too, were unable to satisfy his curiosity about life after death. Finally, Prophet Elijah took pity on Rabbi Chaim, and decided to take him for a ride to the worlds beyond.

After floating in the darkness for many hours, Elijah and the Rabbi arrived in a mysterious great meadow. From afar, they could see numerous people sitting around a huge pot of stew. The aroma was superb, and the Rabbi licked his lips in anticipation. But as they drew nearer, he realized that no one was eating. The people were all tied to their chairs, holding very long spoons. The spoons were simply too long to get the food into their own mouths. Everyone was terribly hungry and irritated. The appetizing smell of the delicacy in front of them only strengthened their torment. This must be Hell, Rabbi Chaim pondered.

The two travelers departed from that awful place, and after a few more hours of flight in total darkness, they arrived in another great meadow, which was oddly similar to the one they had just visited. Here, too, people were sitting around a huge pot of delicious stew. These people were also tied to their chairs and were holding very long spoons. But something was different. Everyone here seemed happy and satisfied. They joked and laughed and sang together.

Rabbi Chaim soon discovered the reason for these people's happiness. They found a way to enjoy the appetizing stew. They simply used the long spoons to feed one another — each scooping a spoonful of stew and delivering it into the mouth of the person across from them. This must be Heaven, Rabbi Chaim realized.

Before returning home, the Rabbi asked Elijah to make one final stop in Hell. He wanted to help the tortured people and teach them how to fill their stomachs despite the long spoons. Upon their arrival, Rabbi Chaim rushed toward the group, shouting and waving his hands: "You do not have to suffer like that! All you have to do is use the long spoons to feed one another!"

But no one paid any attention to the Rabbi's advice. They all continued to sit silently around the large pot, bitter expressions clouding their faces. "Why would I feed any of these horrible people?!" muttered an elderly man in an irate voice. "I'd much rather starve!"

Upon hearing those words, Rabbi Chaim finally understood the real difference between Heaven and Hell.

The Astrologer's Mistake

TWO YOUNG DISCIPLES of Rabbi Hanina visited a well-known astrologer. He examined their faces, read their horoscopes, and even opened a deck of Tarot cards. He then observed them with a grave expression on his face. Unfortunately, he had bad news. The two would not be able to return to their village alive, he predicted.

The youngsters were obviously terrified. But it was getting dark outside, and they had no other choice but to put their trust in God. As they cautiously made their way back to their village, they encountered an old beggar who asked them for food. The disciples carried with them a small sack in which there was a loaf of bread, and they generously cut it in two and divided it with the old man. The beggar thanked them profusely, and the two continued on their way. Soon enough, they reached their village, alive and breathing.

The young disciples were greatly relieved. The astrologer seemed to have been mistaken after all. They washed and prepared for dinner. But when they opened their bread sack they jumped back in surprise. Instead of a half a loaf of bread, half a snake was lying dead inside it.

The King's Portrait

MANY YEARS AGO, in a faraway land, there lived a talented portrait artist. He was patronized by numerous nobles and kings, and the walls of his house were covered with the paintings of his honored customers. There was no collection as magnificent as his in the entire universe. But there was one great king whose portrait the artist did not possess. Indeed, no one owned a painting of that mighty king, for he remained concealed at all times behind a dark curtain.

The artist grew curious about the mysterious veiled king. He asked the sages about him. He learned that the king ruled a country that contained all other countries and lived in a palace that contained all other palaces. He decided to travel to that kingdom, obtain an audience with the great king, and paint his portrait.

His journey was tortuous and lasted many years. He frequently lost his way, and rarely did he encounter people who could point him in the right direction. When he finally reached the secret kingdom, he was an old man.

Once he set foot in the secret kingdom, the artist headed straight to the palace. The guards—impressed with his remarkable unswerving determination—kindly invited him in. The great king was sitting, as always, behind a dark curtain, but he, too, was curious to have a look at the tenacious visitor. He took a quick peek from behind the screen, and just for a short instant, his face was revealed.

The artist jumped back in surprise. He was astounded to discover that the king's face looked rather familiar. In fact, his face was just like his own. After all those years of searching, it seems that the artist had only found himself.

God created man in His own image; in the image of God He created him (Genesis 1:27).

The Fox in the Vineyard

A YOUNG FOX came across a small vineyard surrounded by a tall, thick fence. The fox was hungry, and the smell of the ripe grapes was intoxicating. He circled around the fence for a while until he found a hole in it. Through the hole he could see large clusters of grapes, and his mouth began to water. But unfortunately, the hole was too small for him to pass through. So the crafty fox decided to fast. He stopped eating completely and by the end of the week he was skinny enough to slip through the hole in the fence and into the vineyard.

Once he was inside, the starving fox gorged on the sweet grapes until his stomach hurt. Then he ate some more. Soon he gained back all his weight, and when he wanted to leave the vineyard, he could not pass through the hole in the fence again. He had no other choice but to fast once more. By the end of the week he was skinny enough to slip back out of the vineyard.

The fox stared at the fenced vineyard; his eyes wide open. He was hungry again after many days of fasting. He felt just as he had before coming upon the vineyard in the first place. As the sages say, we come into this world naked and emptyhanded, and we leave it naked and emptyhanded.

Learning to Die

RABBI SIMCHA BUNIM was a well-known Jewish leader in eighteenth-century Poland. After years of service to the community, his time in this world was about to end. Lying ill on his deathbed, he heard his wife crying. She did not want her husband to suffer.

"Don't cry, my dear," the Rabbi comforted his spouse. "There is no need to worry. For all my life I have studied the Bible and the Talmud and have essentially learned just one thing — that is — how to die."

The Bigger Picture

RABBI JOSHUA BEN LEVI fasted for a long time and prayed that Prophet Elijah would take him on one of his journeys throughout the world. One bright night, his prayers were answered, and Elijah appeared in front of him. "I will take you with me," he assured the Rabbi, "but on one condition: that you do not ask any questions all night long."

Rabbi Joshua agreed, and the two flew into the night skies. Before long, they reached a humble house, where a poor family was having a simple supper. Despite their poverty, the family immediately offered great hospitality to the unexpected visitors. They fed them their last loaf of bread and poured them the last of their wine.

The family's most prized possession seemed to have been an old, emaciated cow that helped them plow the fields and gave them milk. But Elijah placed his hand on the cow on their way out, and the poor animal dropped dead.

17

Rabbi Joshua was stunned by this apparent injustice, but he had promised to keep his mouth shut.

Their next destination was an impressive mansion inhabited by the family of a wealthy merchant. The guards refused to let the travelers in at first, but after considerable persuasion they gave them entry to the mansion's kitchen. "Wait here," ordered the wealthy man without offering the guests even a glass of water. "I am having dinner with my family and will talk to you once I am done."

The kitchen was being renovated and bricks from the walls were scattered all over the floor. Elijah placed his hand on the bricks, and the kitchen walls were miraculously restored to perfect condition. Rabbi Joshua felt the burning of injustice in his gut again, but he had sworn not to say a word.

When morning came and the two returned from their journeys, Rabbi Joshua finally mustered the courage to confront Elijah about his actions. "Why did you punish the generous poor family and award the miserly wealthy merchant?" he demanded. "Is that the justice of the prophets?"

"Well," said Elijah, "let me explain, for it is impossible for humans to perceive the bigger picture. The poor farmer was destined to die, so I killed the cow in his stead. As for the miserly merchant—I fixed his walls so that he would not be able to discover the lost treasure hidden in the foundations of his house."

Rabbi Joshua understood. "Mysterious, indeed, are the ways of God," he mumbled.

The Rose and the Thistle

A THISTLE AND A ROSE grew side by side in a wide field. The two plants were friends, but the thistle was always envious of the rose. "We both have thorns," said the thistle to the rose. "So how do you produce such beautiful flowers and I only develop these horrible spiky blossoms?"

The rose did not take his friend's question lightly. He considered it for a long while before answering:

"From the moment I broke out of the seed," he said, "I stretched toward the sun and only had one thought in my mind — *the rose, the rose, the rose*. No matter how hard the winds blew and bent my stalk, not matter how dry I was while waiting for the rains, I kept holding on to that single thought — *the rose, the rose, the rose*. And sure enough, one day I finally produced a beautiful rose."

The Benefit of Folly

IN ANCIENT EGYPT, there lived a learned old man, who flaunted his erudition at every opportunity. He cited the philosophers in nearly every conversation, corrected his neighbors' arguments, and lectured anyone who listened. Such a haughty behavior sure did not make him very popular in the community.

Unfortunately, one cold winter, the learned man's family fell upon hard times. His sons had to go from door to door begging for food. But the neighbors smirked at the learned man's ill fortune. "He thought he knew everything!" they whispered. "But look where the philosophers got him now!"

The learned man's ill fortune took a toll on his physical and mental well-being. Before long, the man went completely mad and danced around half naked in the streets, singing funny songs in strange voices. He became the laughingstock of the whole town.

Sitting on their wide verandah one afternoon, the king and the queen noticed a commotion in the streets below. They learned that a mad man was singing and dancing and ordered he be brought to the palace at once. The mad man continued his clownish behavior inside the palace, and the princes and princesses were delighted. They begged the king to keep him around. So the king offered him a nice room, had him dressed in fine clothes, and served him delicious food. He even provided a royal stipend to his wife and children.

The king's children enjoyed playing with the mad man for several months. Yet, the newly acquired well-being did wonders to the mental health of the man, and soon, he was back to his old ways. He lectured the royal family instead of making them laugh, and the king grew suspicious. "Was he really a mad man or was he just an imposter?" wondered the king. "He must have tricked us in order to live in the palace!"

The angry king banished the man from the palace and ordered that he be punished with forty blows. The learned man was poor again.

Dejected and miserable, he walked back to his humble hut. On his way, he passed next to a synagogue, from which he could hear the rabbi preach the words of King Solomon: "A little folly is worth more than honor and wisdom!"

Clean Language

RABBI CHALFON'S GRANDSON chased a wild chicken in the garden. The chicken was crafty, and the boy was unable to catch it. Panting and sweating, his face all red, he shouted and cursed at the obstinate bird. "You damned XXX chicken!" he yelled. "Just wait and see, your end is coming!"

Rabbi Chalfon observed his grandson's frenzy and called him over to scold him. "You shouldn't speak in anger and use such bad language!" he told him. But the boy did not understand what the fuss was about. "It's only a chicken," he said. "It doesn't even understand what I say!"

"That does not matter," insisted the Rabbi. "When you get angry and curse, your words certainly do not come out of your mouth and go somewhere else," he explained. "Instead, your foul language takes your anger deeper into your own heart. Therefore, in order to preserve a pure heart, you must always keep your language clean."

A Slip of the Tongue

A MIGHTY KING fell ill with a strange disease and the doctors recommended an unusual remedy: the milk of a lioness. The palace announced a reward for the brave person who would be able to obtain such priceless medicine, but most people, of course, were too terrified to try. However, there was one wise man who had a plan.

The man purchased a dozen lambs in the market and hurried to the lioness's den. He placed one lamb in front of the den every few hours, and by the third day, the satiated lioness became so friendly he could pet her. He drew some of her milk into a small bottle and headed back to town.

Midway through his journey, the man stopped for a nap and had a rather peculiar dream. He dreamed that his limbs quarreled with one another. Each believed it deserved the credit for the mission's success. The feet claimed that only due to their ability to walk could the milk have been obtained. The hands argued that without them, the lioness could not have been milked. The eyes objected and reminded everyone that without them, the man could not have found his way to the den in the first place. The brain calmly reasoned that it was responsible for the entire plan. And the tongue disputed them all and boasted: "Without me the man is hopeless!" The others, however, sneered at this. "Quiet, you foolish, boneless thing!" they said. "You contributed nothing!"

The insulted tongue decided to teach them all a lesson. It would show them who was really in charge. And indeed, the following day, the man entered the palace and told the king that he obtained the milk of a snake for him. The king was enraged at this bold disrespect, and ordered that the man's limbs be severed and his eyes gouged out. Upon hearing this, the feet and the hands and the eyes trembled in fear. "Please save us!" they begged the tongue.

Having thus proven its power, the tongue became more considerate. "Forgive me, your honor" said the man to the king. "That was merely a slip of the tongue. I have the milk of a lioness for you." The king drank the milk and

27

was soon cured, and the man learned that the tongue should be regarded with due respect.

Rabbi Gamliel's assistant understood this fable well. When his master sent him to the market and told him to get the best meat he could find, the assistant brought home a tongue.

The next day the Rabbi sent his assistant to the market again, and this time asked him to buy the worst meat he could find. But the assistant returned with tongue again.

Rabbi Gamliel asked him to explain his behavior. "There is nothing better than a good tongue," said the assistant. "But there is nothing worse than an evil tongue!"

The Alias of Evil

WHEN GOD CREATED the universe, she generated both Good and Evil. Good was to spread kindness throughout the world, and Evil was to tempt people to sin, and thus give them free choice. But Evil was unsure how to do his job. "Why would anyone listen to someone called Evil?" he asked God. So God gave him a new name, Snake, so that no one would recognize him as Evil.

It didn't take long for Snake to succeed in his mission. He was quickly able to tempt Adam and Eve to sin by eating the forbidden apple. But the story was soon known throughout the world and everyone recognized the Snake as Evil. Therefore, God gave Evil a new alias, Death, so that no one would recognize him, and he would be able to do his job.

Soon enough, however, people discovered the identity of Death, and kept their distance. God had to change Evil's name again, this time to Satan. But that name did not work either. The Bible clearly revealed him as Evil, and God had to think of yet another new appellation. After some consideration, he decided to name him Arrogance.

Arrogance proved to be a perfect disguise for Evil. Under this new name, Evil was able to penetrate even the houses of the most learned rabbis, the leaders of communities. He was able to sneak into the hearts of the most pious. Only a few were able to recognize Arrogance as Satan, as Death, as Snake, as Evil. Only a few are able to do so to this very day.

Greed

GREED ONCE RAN AROUND TOWN with his right hand tightly closed into a fist. He waved his closed fist in the air for everyone to see, but no one knew what he was holding in it. Whoever saw him quickly ran after him, imagining he possessed what they desired most.

Some, indeed, were eventually able to catch Greed, to tackle him, and pin him to the ground. They forced Greed to open his fist. But when he finally did, it was empty.

The Good of the Many

ONCE UPON A TIME, there lived a benevolent king who worked hard to make his city attractive and comfortable for its citizens. He supervised the construction of roads and schools, he administered the planting of trees and flowers, but when he had the earth dug in search of water, not a single drop was found.

The concerned king summoned a world-famous hydrologist—a specialist in finding underground water even in the driest regions—and asked him for help. The hydrologist walked around town and inspected the ground. In a few days he found the right spot. "If you dig here," he told the king, "a great gush of water will come out." But there was one problem. The spot was located right in the middle of a populated neighborhood, and the water was likely to flood several houses. The king thought it over and nonetheless decided to have a well dug there. After all, a few houses may be destroyed but there is no life without water.

Now that the city had roads, schools, gardens, and water, there was only one thing missing: a hospital. For living in a place with no doctors was indeed precarious. So the king invited a world-famous physician—a medicine man who interned in the most outstanding institutions—and asked him to come and work in his town.

The citizens all came out into the streets to welcome the distinguished medicine man. They rejoiced for having such a great doctor at their disposal. A man with a slight headache volunteered to be the first patient. The doctor took him into his clinic, but after a few days the man died.

The citizens took to the streets, angry. "This is no doctor but the Angel of Death himself!" they raged. So the king summoned the physician and asked him for an explanation. "How could you let a person with a simple headache die?" he demanded.

But the doctor remained calm. "When I came into this city, I noticed that everyone was eating whatever they wanted, drinking profusely, and smoking in chains," he explained. "No one worried about getting ill as they trusted me to cure them. Thus, in order to terrify the entire town, I did not save the man. That way, people would learn to take care of their own health and avoid illnesses."

The king was astonished. "Was this the right approach?" he wondered. "Is the life of a man the same as digging a well?"

Winemaking

IN THE YEARS FOLLOWING the Great Flood, Noah had to break ground and cultivate all kinds of new plants. When he first planted a vineyard, the Devil arrived and offered his help. Noah naively agreed, and when he looked the other way, the Devil fertilized the soil with the blood of slaughtered lambs, lions, pigs, and monkeys.

When the grapes ripened and were made into wine, the Devil smiled wickedly to himself. He knew what was coming. Now if people drank one glass of wine, they would become as weak and docile as a lamb; if they drank two glasses, they would feel as daring and audacious as a lion; if they drank three glasses, they would become as nasty as pigs; and if they drank four glasses, they would dance foolishly like monkeys. The Devil's work was done.

A Sack of Stones

A TIRED-LOOKING FELLOW approached the rabbi after the evening prayers. He asked him to be excused from the morning assemblies at the synagogue. "I work hard all day long and barely get enough sleep at night. It is just too taxing to wake up so early each morning to pray," he complained.

The rabbi was sympathetic to the man's troubles. After all, it was surely not easy to abide by the six hundred and thirteen commandments listed in the Talmud. "Let me tell you a story," he said finally.

"Once there was a poor stonecutter who pounded rocks all day long. One day, as he walked back to the village with a large sack of stones on his hunched back, he came upon a friend. 'This sack is so heavy,' he grumbled. 'Look! It is full of rocks.' He opened his sack and showed his load to his friend. But after examining the stones for a short while, his friend jumped back in surprise. 'Wow!' he yelled.

'These are not regular stones; they are unpolished diamonds!' He scraped off some of the dust from a stone and showed it to the stonecutter. It was shiny and bright."

"Once the stonecutter realized he was carrying a sack of diamonds on his back," continued the rabbi, "the load did not feel heavy or burdensome any longer. He lifted it with ease and ran back home feeling happy and free."

It's All for the Best

RABBI AKIVA TRAVELED to far lands and took with him three things: a donkey to ride, a rooster to wake him early for prayer, and a candle to light up the dark. In the evening, he arrived in a small town and looked for a lodging house to spend the night. But alas, the only hotel in town was full, and the Rabbi had to camp in the nearby fields.

"Thank God, I'm sure it's all for the best," said Rabbi Akiva to himself. "After all, it's cool and breezy outside, and I have the animals by my side!"

But as soon as the Rabbi settled for bed, he heard a loud roar from the bushes. Before he knew it, a lion jumped out and quickly devoured the poor donkey.

"Thank God, I'm sure it's all for the best," Rabbi Akiva comforted himself. "The poor donkey was unfortunately killed, but I am still here, and perhaps I might be able to get a few hours of sleep."

But as soon as the Rabbi shut his eyes, he heard another wail from close by, and a wild cat jumped out and grabbed the rooster. The Rabbi was stunned, but he thought to himself: "It's probably also all for the best. At least I will not have to wake up so early."

Rabbi Akiva was now all alone and a little anxious, so he tried to light up his candle. But the stubborn winds blew the light away, and the Rabbi remained in absolute darkness. "Thank God, this too is all for the best," he murmured, "for in the dark it's surely easier to get some rest."

The exhausted Rabbi slept like a log and, in the morning, he was woken by a local farmer. "Haven't you heard what happened last night?" asked the farmer. "A group of bandits rampaged through town, pillaging and assaulting everyone. I hid in my barn and just barely escaped!"

"How lucky I was!" cried out Rabbi Akiva. "If I slept in town, if the donkey brayed, if the rooster cackled, and if the candle lighted, the bandits would have gotten to me as well. Thank God, it was truly all for the best!"

The Mountains of Israel

A RUMOR HAD SPREAD across the land: God was about to bestow the Law on humankind. It was said that the ceremony would take place on the top of a mighty mountain, but no one knew exactly where. The summits of Israel were all excited, hoping that God would descend onto them. Soon they began to quarrel.

"I am the highest mountain in the land of Israel!" announced Mt. Hermon. "I reach into the clouds and I am covered in snow — surely God would choose me for the ceremony!"

"That cannot be!" argued Mt. Moriah. "Height does not matter as much as sanctity, and I am the holiest summit in the land! After all, I was designated to house the Holy Temple!"

"Sure, you two are high and holy," agreed Mt. Carmel, "but I am the most beautiful mountain in the entire region. I am always covered in flowers and greenery, and the vista of the sea I offer from my peak is truly breathtaking! There is no doubt I would be perfect for such a glorious ceremony."

Only Mt. Sinai stayed out of the dispute. It knew it was neither high nor pretty. No snow was found on its peaks and no flowers decorated its slopes. It was stumpy, parched, and scorching hot. It did not think it had what it took to host such a godly ceremony.

But God, as always, had other plans. "It is neither stature nor appearance, but humility that I respect!" he said. "While all the mountains bragged and boasted, only Mt. Sinai remained humble and modest, so let it be a lesson to the people of the world—on bare Mt. Sinai I will bestow the Law!"

Two Wives

THERE WAS ONCE A GREEDY MAN who was discontent with having only one wife. He was married for thirty years, and his wife had long lost her youthful charms. He still loved her dearly, of course, but for him that was not enough. So he went out to town and convinced a young woman from a poor household to marry him at once.

The man was pleased having two wives at first, but he soon realized it was not as easy as it seemed. His new youthful wife kept plucking all the white hair from his head because she wanted him to look younger. His first wife, however, plucked all his remaining dark hair as she wanted him to look older. And before long, the greedy man was left completely bald.

A Break from Learning

RABBI SHALOM SHAR'ABI was on his way to the seminary when he noticed a blind woman walking barefoot in the rain. A baby, soaking wet and crying, was resting on her shoulder. He pitied the poor woman, covered her with his raincoat, and led her to his house.

After the woman had warmed up, put her baby to sleep, and eaten some soup, she asked the kind stranger his name. Rabbi Shar'abi was the well-known leader of the entire community and was thus hesitant to reveal his identity. But the woman insisted.

The blind woman jumped to her feet in embarrassment once she heard the name of her host. "I am sorry for taking so much of your time," she apologized. "I know you must be very busy studying Talmud and Mishna and teaching the youth."

But the Rabbi gently led her back to her seat. "On the contrary," he said. "I should be thanking you! I have been studying the Law for years and only today I finally had a chance to test my learning. For only one who is able to take a break from his work in order to help others is a true student of God."

Nothing to Worry About

THE MAN SITTING next to the rabbi on the train seemed terribly restless. He moaned and groaned and stared blankly through the window. When the rabbi asked him what was bothering him, he explained that his only son was being recruited to the military. "He is taking the physical exam as we speak," he said, his face pale from worry.

"But that is nothing to worry about!" The rabbi comforted the man with a big smile. "For your son might still fail the physical exam and not be recruited after all!"

The troubled man nodded his head, unconvinced.

"And even if he passes the exam and joins the military, no war is likely to break out in the near future, so there is no need to worry!"

The troubled man measured the rabbi quietly with his eyes, trying to judge whether his optimism was sincere.

"And even if war does break out, most soldiers are able to return home safe and sound. So there is no need to worry!" continued the rabbi.

"And even if your son will be injured in a war, we have good doctors and he may still heal. So there is no need to worry!"

Now the rabbi had the full attention of the troubled fellow, who turned away from the window and stared straight at the optimistic religious man.

"And even if your son is injured and dies from his wounds, he may still go to Heaven! For going to Heaven does not depend on luck but on his own actions. So just ask him to be good, and there is nothing to worry about at all!"

Holier Than Thou

THERE WAS ONCE A RIGHTEOUS MAN who regarded all sexual temptation as sin. He wished to rid himself of worldly desire and come closer to God. He stopped sharing the bed with his wife, but that was hardly helpful. Lustful thoughts continued to haunt him.

He decided to camp out in the garden. But whenever he came into the house to get a book or a slice of bread, he saw his wife and the demons of desire took hold of his thoughts. He realized that the only solution would be to live as a hermit, all by himself.

The righteous man walked for days in the desert until he found the perfect spot. It was silent and peaceful and solitary. No other living being was violating the vast emptiness. The man felt his lust was melting away. But one night, desire snuck back into his dreams. The frustrated man did not know what to do next.

He finally resolved to fast. He stopped eating for days, and sure enough his lust gradually subsided. His dreams were pure. His emaciated body grew lighter and lighter, until one day it simply drifted with the wind up into the sky. The righteous man rose above the clouds and the stars, and eventually reached the highest of Heavens.

Dazed up in Heaven, the man suddenly saw a woman. She was the most beautiful creature he had ever laid eyes on. Her allure was overpowering, and the man reached out to embrace her. But as he held her, he began to fall. He quickly dropped and descended from that high abode, and some say that he is still falling to this very day.

Dancing Jews

HASSIDIC JEWS ARE KNOWN for dancing and singing at every opportunity. The famous founder of the Hassidic movement, HaBa'al Shem Tov, was once asked about the reason for this. The Rabbi responded with a parable:

"Once upon a time, a traveling musician came to town. He took his place in the central plaza and began playing his instrument. His talent was boundless and, before long, people began to gather and listen to the divine music. The melody was enchanting, and the spectators could not help but move their bodies to the beat."

"But when a deaf man walked by, he was quite surprised at this commotion in the middle of the street. 'What is going on here?' he murmured. 'Why are all those people twisting and shaking?'"

"In the same way the Hassidic ears are attuned to the divine melody of God," explained HaBa'al Shem Tov. "They cultivate sensitivity to the music of Creation and can't help it but move their bodies to its rhythm. But others are deaf to these celestial sounds. They are unable to hear the music and are thus astounded by the odd behavior of the dancing Jews.

The Castle of Riches

ONCE UPON A TIME, a great wise king built a magnificent castle in order to secure his most brilliant riches. He had the castle surrounded by high walls and deep tunnels, and placed fierce guards at its gates. The great luster of his treasures disappeared behind these towering barriers. Only the bravest of men attempted to reach them.

Most were discouraged simply by looking at the great walls of the castle. They did not believe they had the necessary strength to penetrate them. Some succeeded in crossing the first gate, but turned back upon encountering the second wall, which appeared to be as high as the clouds. Others came closer to the castle but ended up drowning in a tunnel. Many were shooed away by a threatening guard.

But a few fearless men were eventually able to cross all obstacles and enter the formidable castle. Inside, they found themselves surrounded by inconceivable riches, far beyond their imagination. But now, when they looked back toward the way from which they had come, they saw no walls or guards at all. A beautiful terrain filled with flowering gardens and orchids stretched as far as their eyes could see. It seemed to have been there all along.

Falsehood and Blight

EVERYONE PAIRED UP and rushed to get a seat in Noah's ark. The Great Flood was approaching, and no one wanted to remain outside. The lion paired with a lioness, the cow found herself a bull, and the horse arrived with a mare. Only Falsehood came running and sweating all by himself.

Falsehood was having difficulty finding a partner for the ride. He asked Blessing, but she was already taken by Success. He tried Joy, but she would not replace her mate, Satisfaction, for the world. In desperation, he finally decided to invite the unattractive Blight.

"Would you be my partner?" he asked her. "The rains are coming and only couples are allowed into the ark."

But Blight was suspicious. This was Falsehood after all. "What would you give me if I agree?" she asked. "Please come," Falsehood replied, "and everything I achieve in my life would be yours." Blight accepted his proposal and the two of them stepped into the ark.

A year later the rains were gone. The sun was shining, and everyone stepped out of the ark. Falsehood soon hurried to conduct his business, and Blight followed him close behind. He lied and he cheated, committed fraud and embezzled, but everything he achieved was immediately taken by Blight.

Poor Falsehood! Despite his numerous endeavors, he remained deprived and abject throughout his life. All his lies were for nothing. They only contributed to Blight.

A Mosquito in the Head

ROMAN EMPEROR TITUS was mighty and brutal. He conquered Jerusalem, destroyed the Holy Temple, and commanded his soldiers to collect the sacred vessels and take them back to Rome. During his journey home, however, a small mosquito flew into his nose and got stuck inside his head.

The mosquito kept growing inside Titus's head and the buzzing was awful. His head hurt day and night and he could not think straight. It was plain torture. One morning, his chariot passed near a blacksmith's shop, and he soon realized that the loud pounding of the smith soothed his constant headache. It was so noisy outside that the buzzing in his head could not be heard.

Titus ordered that blacksmith shops be built all around the palace. The deafening clamor silenced the mosquito in his head, and

Titus felt considerably better. But each time the pounding of the workers stopped, even for a mere second, the noise in the Emperor's head felt louder than ever.

The Love of God

A GROUP OF YOUNG and devout Hassids once came across a man who was praying late at night. The correct time for the evening prayers had long passed, and the righteous Hassids reproached the praying man:

"Imagine that one day your wife cooked your breakfast in the afternoon," they told him. "You would certainly be starving by then. Would you accept such lateness peacefully? That is why we must pray at the right time!"

The praying man smiled kindly at the angry youth. "You must not understand a man's love for his wife," he finally told them. "For a man who truly loves his wife would not mind a simple lateness. He would not even mind if she did not cook his breakfast at all," he said. "And that is the way God loves me."

The Outcome of Jealousy

A LONG TIME AGO, a simple merchant traveled far from home on business. While sailing the high seas, he was caught in a terrible storm. Shaking with fear, he started to pray, begging God to save him due to the benevolence of his wife. "My wife is such a good person," he pleaded with God. "Please save me from the storm so I can care for her livelihood!"

A fellow traveler heard the prayer of the merchant and laughed to himself. "Do you really believe your wife is waiting for you all by herself during your travels?" he asked him. "I am sure she can be easily tempted to meet other men!"

The merchant's face reddened with anger. "You clearly do not know my wife!" he cried out. "She would never do that!"

"I'll tell you what," answered the devious traveler. "I will go and test your wife's loyalty. If I am able to return with her wedding ring, you will know that my temptation was successful and present me with half of your merchandise."

The merchant grudgingly agreed. He was in no mood for an argument and trusted his wife completely. "It does not matter," he said to himself. "He can try all he wants, but my wife will never come close to such a man."

And he was right. The merchant's wife did not even care to look at the man's face. He tried to bring her presents, sing songs beneath her window, but nothing worked. So he hired a thief to steal her ring. He then showed the ring to the stunned merchant and received half of his merchandise.

When the fuming merchant returned home, he could not even bear to look at his wife. He loved her dearly but his jealously took over his heart. He fought with her bitterly and spent his nights on the couch. His wife decided to go and stay with her parents for a while. The chariot driver who took her there was kind and handsome, and they fell in love.

Babies and Thieves

RABBI DOV BER OF MEZERITCH was a well-known itinerant preacher in eighteenth-century Europe. He was celebrated for his creative spirit and for not sticking to convention. When his disciples wished to imitate the behaviors of the Hebrew sages, Rabbi Dov Ber instructed them to learn from babies and thieves instead:

"There are three things you should learn from babies," he told his students. "To be completely happy, to cry with all your heart, and to never sit around idly."

"But that is not all," he continued. "There are seven things you should learn from thieves! The first is to do your good work at night, privately, secretly, without showing off or bragging about it. The second is to not give up easily: if you fail the first night, always try again the next. The third is to stick together and help one another. The fourth thing you should learn from thieves is to be willing to give up your life at any second. The fifth is be ready to sell cheaply whatever you obtain to anyone who needs it. The sixth is the power to withstand all torture and beating without giving up your mind. And the last thing you should learn from thieves is to love your work despite all criticism. For that is the right attitude in working for the Creator!"

Condolences

WHEN THE SON OF RABBI YOCHANAN BEN
ZAKAI died, his closest disciples hurried over to
comfort him. Sitting in front of their mourning
teacher, they did not know what to say. After a
long silence, one of the students finally spoke:

"Please accept my condolences," he said.
"As you know, even the son of Adam—the first
man on Earth—died young," he tried to comfort
his teacher.

"Thank you," replied the Rabbi, "but
your words have made me twice as sad! For
now I mourn not only the death of my own son,
but also the death of the son of Adam."

Before long, a second student
approached Rabbi Yochanan. "All of Job's sons
died in a single day, and still he did not lose
faith," he reminded his teacher.

But that did not comfort the mourning
Rabbi at all. "Thank you for your words," he
said, "but now I feel sorry for Job as well!"

A third student reminded his teacher that although the two sons of Aaron died in one day, Aaron kept his peace. But that, too, did not console the grieving Rabbi. "Now I bemoan Aaron's sons as well," he said.

"When King David's son died, he consoled his wife straight away," whispered a fourth disciple, clearly oblivious to the earlier failures of his fellow students. "King David and his queen soon had another baby, and he became King!" he added.

But the Rabbi would not be comforted. "Now I lament King David's son, too," he said.

Finally, a fifth student helped his teacher up from his seat and led him to the bathhouse. After the Rabbi freshened up, his student told him a story:

"Once there was an almighty king, who deposited his greatest treasure for safekeeping in the hands of a simple man. The man was always anxious to protect the treasure and keep it safe and sound. After all, one must beware of losing the possessions of a great king. The man knew that a king's treasure should be returned in pristine condition, wholesome and untainted.

And when it was finally time to return the treasure, the king was glad to receive it in an immaculate state. "

Upon hearing this tale, tears dropped from the eyes of Rabbi Yochanan. Now he felt a little better.

When Rabbi Levi's son died, he followed his coffin to the burial ground in song and dance. His relatives were appalled and asked him to cease his folly at once. But Rabbi Levi would not stop. "I brought a pure soul into this world," he told them, "and I am glad I was able to return it just as pure."

Suffering in Heaven

WHEN RABBI ELIMELECH WEISBLUM passed away and stood before the courts of Heaven, he was asked whether he prayed every day at the correct times. His answer, unfortunately, was "no". He was then asked whether he studied the Bible and the Talmud throughout his life. His answer, again, was a contrite "no." He gave another negative answer when asked whether he donated to the poor. "Well then," he was sternly told, "we must send you to Hell."

But there must have been some mistake. Because Rabbi Elimelech soon found himself standing up in Heaven. He stared at the joys surrounding him and could not believe his eyes. He knew he did not deserve it. He hung his head in shame, feeling guiltier than ever. Some say Rabbi Elimelech is still standing up in Heaven, embarrassed and uncomfortable, glaring blankly at the ground, to this very day.

Matchmaking

A WEALTHY MATRON listened to Rabbi Yose Ben Halafta's sermon about the Creation of the world. After the talk, she quickly approached the Rabbi and asked: "And what has this almighty God been doing ever since the Creation? Doesn't he see the suffering we endure in it?"

The Rabbi smiled at the cynical woman. "Well, God has been considerably busy all this time matching couples together," he told her.

"Ha!" dismissed the old lady. "Such an easy job! I could do that much myself without breaking a sweat. Just wait and see, I will show you!" she promised the Rabbi.

The next day, the wealthy matron lined up her numerous servants and matched them into couples. She considered their ages, their looks, their personalities, and their dispositions. "From now on you shall live together and learn to enjoy each other's company," she commanded. Then she sent them on their way.

But in the following weeks her servants began to behave oddly. Some seemed tired and depressed, others came to work with broken limbs and black eyes, and yet others simply ran away. They all begged to be separated from their mates.

The matron reconsidered the words of Rabbi Yose. Perhaps God has been keeping busy all along. For matching couples in love was a task worthy of Heaven.

Speech and Silence

TWO PHILOSOPHERS DEBATED at the court of Roman Emperor Hadrian. One was arguing in favor of speech, and the other in favor of silence.

The oratory skills of the advocate of speech were superb. In a loud, clear voice, he reasoned that no society could persist and flourish without a spoken language. The spectators clapped their hands in agreement.

Then his adversary, the reserved supporter of silence, opened his mouth to speak. But before he could do so, the advocate of speech hit him on his mouth and injured his tongue.

"Why did you do that?" demanded Emperor Hadrian.

"I did it because he tried to use my weapon in order to defend his argument!" explained the advocate of speech.

At that moment, an old rabbi stepped out of the crowd. He asked the Emperor for permission to speak in favor of the bruised man. "When people praise silence, they do not mean that one should be completely quiet as a mute!" announced the rabbi. "One should certainly communicate with others. Yet, he or she should stay silent at the right times and in the correct situations!"

"When others argue or slander in front of us, for example, silence is unquestionably better than speech," concluded the rabbi. It was only then that he realized the irony of his assertions.

A Very Tall Man

A VERY TALL MAN stood in the heat of the sun. His head was raised up so high in the sky it almost jarred into the sun's orbit. It was scorching hot up there, and the tall man was drained and exhausted.

A compassionate short man noticed the suffering of the giant. He wanted to help. He decided to sit in front of him and drink from a jar of cool refreshing water, expecting the tall man to learn from his example and do the same. But the giant did not take the hint. From his great altitude he could barely see the short man. He would certainly not stoop down so low in order to take a closer look.

But the compassionate man would not give up. He tried splashing some water at the tall man. When that did not have much effect, he ran and fetched a long hose and started sprinkling water up toward him. But the giant bolted his mouth and tightened his lips. He would not accept such pity from those beneath. The water simply rained back down and cooled the compassionate short man. And the very tall man eventually dehydrated and died.

The Four Kings of Judea

BEFORE LAUNCHING AN ATTACK on his enemies, King David always prayed to God. He requested God's assistance in pursuing and overtaking his adversaries. And sure enough, great conquests followed.

Decades after the death of King David, Asa took over the Kingdom of Judea. But King Asa was not nearly as mighty as his forefather had been. Since he was unable to subdue his foes in battle like David had done, he needed to pray in a different way. Before going to war, he simply entreated God to protect him from harm. And sure enough, God did.

When Asa's son, Jehoshaphat, took the throne, Judea was no longer the powerful kingdom it once was. Jehoshaphat was unable to conquer his enemies as King David had done, and he was not even able to defend himself as his father had done. All he could do before heading to the battlefield was chant hymns in praise of the Lord. And sure enough, these prayers kept him safe.

Two-hundred years of relative calm passed before Hezekiah became King of Judea. Hezekiah was a rather frail ruler, but his faith was forceful and unwavering. When the enemy forces were approaching, he neither pursued them nor attempted to gather troops for defense. He did not even strain his voice in songs of praise. All he did was lie in his bed and trust God to protect his people. And sure enough, God did.

A Diamond Ring

THE GENEROSITY OF RABBI SHMELKE HOROWITZ was known all over the town of Nikolsburg. Every week, before the Sabbath, beggars showed up at his doorstep asking for alms, and the Rabbi rewarded them with an open hand and a joyful heart.

On one rainy Friday afternoon, a hungry vagrant knocked on Rabbi Shmelke's door. His soiled clothes hung from his emaciated flesh, and the Rabbi hurried inside to fetch some money. But unfortunately, he seemed to have already given away all his cash to those who showed up earlier. The Rabbi did not have many possessions, and he could not think of a single thing he could hand out to the poor man. Then he suddenly spotted his wife's wedding ring lying on the kitchen table. Without a second thought, he grabbed it and offered it to the man at the door.

The Rabbi stepped back inside and told his wife about the ring. His wife nodded her head at him and smiled. "I do not mind the ring itself," she told him, "but the diamond set in it is rather rare. It must be very expensive!" Upon hearing this, Rabbi Shmelke jumped to his feet and bolted out the door to see if he could still find the poor vagrant.

Fortunately, the Rabbi was able to catch up with the poor man not far from the house. "There is something I must tell you!" he yelled to the startled beggar. "A rare diamond is set in the ring I just gave you. You must be careful not to sell it too cheaply, it is very expensive!"

Books

ONE SUMMER EVENING, HaBa'al Shem Tov strolled leisurely back home from the synagogue. The weather was amicable, and the Rabbi enjoyed the fresh air. Next to the river, he noticed one of his young disciples sitting on a bench, reading a book. The youngster was so engrossed in the book that he did not even notice his teacher passing by. "What are you reading so avidly?" enquired the Rabbi.

"Why, it is the book you have written!" replied the student. "Surely you must recognize it!"

HaBa'al Shem Tov seemed rather confused. He glanced at the book and frowned. He could not remember writing anything, or was it just the amnesia of old age? No! It must have been one of his students that had written down his words. "Let me have a look at this," the Rabbi said to the youngster.

HaBa'al Shem Tov opened the book and browsed attentively through its pages. He noticed his name written in bold on the cover, surveyed the chapter titles, and examined some of the quotes. Finally, he started laughing. "There is not a single word here that I actually said!" he cried out. "Even this very story was not really taught by me!"

King Solomon and the Queen of Ants

GOD ENDOWED KING SOLOMON with marvelous gifts and talents. He gave him a flying carpet made of silk so he could travel and survey the entire world. He also equipped him with the ability to speak and understand the languages of all living beings.

Soaring from city to city, having breakfast in Syria and dinner in India, King Solomon once floated over a large colony of ants. From his carpet up in the air, he could hear the queen of the ants order her subjects to hide away from the King. Thousands of ants scattered and disappeared in seconds.

"Why did you have to do that?" King Solomon shouted toward the queen of the ants. "I'm sure you know that I have no intention to harm you!"

"I wasn't worried that you were going to kill us," answered the ant queen. "I just didn't want my subjects to look up to you and learn to be proud!"

"What did you say?" yelled the King. "I can't hear you very well from up here!"

"Well then," replied the ant in a loud voice, "why don't you lift me up and take me closer?"

King Solomon reached his hand down and took the tiny creature in his palm. The King and the ant flew up high on the magical silk carpet and gazed at the world below. "Can any creature fly any higher?" King Solomon asked the ant. "Is there anyone greater than myself in the entire world?"

The little ant queen smiled to herself. "Please forgive me for saying this," she blurted, "but it seems that even I am greater than you are! After all, you have gone through all this trouble just to carry me up into the sky!"

A Four-Horse Carriage

ONCE UPON A TIME, Rabbi Israel and Rabbi Meir stumbled into each other accidentally on the road to Lvov. Rabbi Israel was sitting in a luxurious carriage tied to four stout stallions, while Rabbi Meir came riding in a simple carriage harnessed to a feeble-looking donkey. The sun was setting, and the two Rabbis stepped down to pray at the side of the road.

After praying, Rabbi Israel pointed at the muddy path and offered his friend one of his stallions. "If you get stuck in the mud, your donkey will not be able to pull you out," he warned Rabbi Meir. "That is the reason I keep these sturdy stallions and expensive carriage. If I get stuck, they will pull me out easily."

Rabbi Meir thanked his friend for the kind offer. "You are very generous, but I must decline your offer," he said. "I ride in a simple carriage harnessed to an old donkey because it forces me to stay watchful of pitfalls in the road. That way, I can avoid any trouble."

Debating with a Bandit

NEARLY TWO THOUSAND YEARS AGO, Rabbi Yochanan was head rabbi of Tiberius. He was highly cultured, greatly learned, and rather fine-looking. One day, the notorious bandit Rish Lakish saw the Rabbi bathing in the Jordan River and mistook him for a beautiful young woman. The excited bandit took off his clothes and briskly jumped into the water.

Rish Lakish advanced vigorously toward the Rabbi, but as soon as he came close, he realized his mistake. "A beauty like yours is suitable for a woman not for a man!" the disappointed bandit cried out. "You shouldn't be bathing here and teasing people in vain!"

The Rabbi looked at the bandit and covered his private parts with his palms. "A vigor like yours is suitable for learning not for robbing!" he laughed. "I'll tell you what," he continued, "if you come study with me, I will introduce you to my sister, who is even more attractive than I am!"

The beauty of Rabbi Yochanan's sister was known throughout the land, and Rish Lakish could not refuse such an offer. He left his gang and began to study diligently with the Rabbi. Eventually he married the Rabbi's sister and became a learned and respected member of the community.

But one day, an argument erupted between the Rabbi and his new brother-in-law. The disagreement involved the purification of a knife after it has been used to butcher an animal. Rabbi Yochanan argued that it should be purified by fire, and Rish Lakish insisted that it be purified by water. The two argued continuously for weeks and months, until one day the debate turned into a quarrel. "You talk about knives with such certainty," blurted the Rabbi, "that it seems like the bandit is still inside you!"

Rish Lakish was greatly offended. He left the study hall and returned to his old gang. Soon later, he died in a knife fight.

When Rabbi Yochanan heard of the bandit's death, sorrow and remorse clouded his entire being. His students tried to console him. They listened eagerly to all his teachings and willingly accepted all his arguments.

But the Rabbi would not stand it. This sort of study was futile. He missed Rish Lakish and the fervent debates he had with him, which only expanded their wisdom. But he knew that the fire of their debates also ruined their friendship. The agitated Rabbi decided to cool himself in the water of the Jordan River. But the currents were strong, and within minutes, he drowned.

Peace and Truth

WHEN GOD WAS PREPARING to create humankind, he summoned his angels and asked for their opinions. He hoped they would all take part in the Creation, but unfortunately, they began to argue.

The Angel of Truth was hesitant to accept God's plans. "Please do not create humans," he said. "For they will be full of lies and deceit!"

But the Angel of Benevolence disagreed. "Please do create humans," he cried out. "For they will be charitable and kind!"

Then the Angel of Peace barged in. "Please do not create humans," he said. "For they will be irritable and quarrelsome."

But the Angel of Justice was quick to reply. "Please do create humans!" he demanded. "For they will be fair and just."

God listened to his angels carefully and mulled over their suggestions. Finally, He grabbed the Angel of Truth and cast him away. It seems that they cannot all get along, He considered. Perhaps it would be better, then, if humans would be dishonest and lie, but be able to live in peace and harmony.

The Coal Miner

ONCE UPON A TIME, a poor coal miner was digging in a pit when he suddenly noticed a large shining rock. It was very pretty and appeared to be expensive. The lucky miner took the gem to an expert and was told it was worth a fortune. But in order to find an affluent buyer for it, he would have to sail to the capital of the kingdom.

The miner worried that he would not be able to pay the price of the boat ride to the capital. But once he showed the captain his gem, he was welcomed on board right away. The most luxurious cabin was prepared immediately for the rich passenger who had such a magnificent gem in his possession, and he was invited to sit at the captain's table at mealtimes.

Over succulent dishes and refined wines, the miner and the captain soon became friends. But as the miner returned to his cabin one night, the gem was missing. As it turned out, the cleaning staff did not realize its worth and threw it away with the rest of the garbage. The expensive gem was now lost, lying at the bottom of the sea.

The poor miner was miserable and anxious. He knew he would not be able to pay for any of the luxuries he enjoyed on the boat. The next evening, he sat quietly during dinner, pondering his dejected state. But before he could say anything, the captain offered him a business deal. "Let me invest my money in your trade," the captain offered. "That way, we can both make more money in the capital!" He took out his wallet, wrote down an incredulous number on a check, and handed it to the miner. The two friends shook hands.

However, life is unpredictable, and soon after the boat anchored in the capital's port, the captain incurred a strange disease and passed away. The miner was left with the captain's money. Nothing he possessed ever belonged to him, yet he lived on.

King Solomon's Meals

KING SOLOMON TOOK NUMEROUS WIVES and thus lost favor with God. His kingdom fell, and the King was reduced to poverty. He wandered the streets of Jerusalem, knocking on doors and begging for food.

One evening, a well-dressed man opened his door to Solomon and invited him in. "Oh, you pitiful thing!" he said upon laying his eyes on the bony former King. "Come inside, I will prepare a feast worthy of Kings especially for you!"

And indeed, the meal was delightful. Famished Solomon gorged on the delicious food as his host observed in satisfaction. "Does this meal not remind you of your days in the palace?" he asked Solomon. "Oh, it must have been great being a king!" he remarked. But these memories saddened Solomon greatly, and the remorseful ex-King began to sob. He had now lost his appetite, and before long, he got up and left.

The next day, a simple man saw Solomon sitting on the side of the road and invited him to his house for a meal. After the events of the previous night, Solomon was reluctant at first, but the pangs in his stomach convinced him to follow the kind stranger. Once they reached his humble hut, the host placed a bowl of soup in front of Solomon and tried to console him. "You must be going through a difficult period," he told him. "But I'm sure God will soon make you king again!" The simple vegetable soup that was served tasted better than the most refined dishes Solomon had ever placed in his mouth. He asked for seconds.

Solomon was eventually returned to the throne and his sayings were recorded in the Bible. Recalling the simple soup he had eaten during his turbulent period, the King proclaims in the Book of Proverbs: "Better a dish of vegetables where there is love, than a fattened ox with hatred."

Father and Children

A FATHER AND HIS CHILDREN rode their carriage on a country road. It was a beautiful day and they enjoyed the fresh air. The sweet scents of flowers and wild berries tickled their nostrils. The children could not resist the sugary aroma and asked their father to take a break so they could gather some fruit. "Sure thing," smiled the Father, "but hurry up so we can get home before dark."

The children ran off happily into the surrounding forest looking for berries. But after a long while had passed, the Father began to worry. "Why don't you come back?" he shouted toward the woods. "We should probably get going!" Yet, the children were so engrossed in their culinary pleasures that they barely noticed their Father's calling.

The Father stepped off the carriage and found his children sitting under a tree, gorging on rosy berries. They looked so happy his heart sank. He loved his children very much and understood their innocent passions. "We can stay here as long as you wish," he told them softly. "But please call out 'Father!' 'Father!' every so often, just to let me know you are nearby. After all, we don't want you to get lost in the woods, do we?"

And that is the reason we pray.

The One-Eyed Skull

IN ONE OF HIS MANY TRAVELS, Alexander the Great stumbled upon the gates of Paradise. He pounded on the large doors and begged the guards to let him in. "I am a great King!" he chided them. "You must grant me entrance!"

But the stern guards were unfazed. "Only the most righteous are allowed access to this place," they insisted. "But since you are such an important man," they added, "here is a little gift for you." They opened the Gates of Paradise slightly and threw out a skull with one fleshy eye toward Alexander.

The skull was extremely heavy, and the perplexed King decided to weigh it. Maybe it was worth something after all. He placed the skull on scales and balanced it with pure gold, but no matter how much gold he added, the skull still weighed heavier.

The King summoned all the wise sages of the land, but no one could explain the mystery of the heavy skull. Finally, one old man came forward and advised the King to cover the eye of the skull with mud. Alexander grasped a handful of dirt and covered the eye of the skull, and indeed, it immediately became much lighter. Now even a small piece of gold weighed heavier than the skull on the scales.

Everyone stared at the old man expecting an explanation for the mysterious behavior of the skull. The old man looked back and smiled. "Why, it is quite simple," he said. "For the human eye will not be satisfied with any amount of gold, until it is covered with the earth of its grave!"

The Two Brothers and the Holy Temple

ONCE UPON A TIME, two loving brothers inherited a wheat field in Jerusalem from their father. One of the brothers had a wife and several children, and the other was single and childless. They worked the field together all winter and split the crops between them in spring. By the time they went to bed on the first day of summer, a pile of grains was stacked at either side of the field, each equal to the other.

The single brother tossed and turned in his bed all night. This was not fair, he thought. After all, his brother had to feed an entire family and certainly needed more grains than he did. The single brother could not bear this injustice. He decided to get up and secretly move some of his grains to the pile on the other side of the field.

However, the single brother was not the only one awake that night. His brother also lay in bed with his eyes open for hours. This was not fair, he thought. All his brother had in the world was his work, and so at the very least he deserved to enjoy the fruit of his labors to the fullest. He got up quietly in the dark, careful not to wake his wife, and transferred some of his grains to the pile on the other side of the field.

When morning came and the brothers stepped outside, they were both surprised to discover that the two piles of grains remained equal. And so the same ordeal took place again the next night, and then the next. But the piles remained the same. Until one night, the two brothers stumbled into each other in the middle of the field, stalks of grain in their hands.

King Solomon was deeply moved upon hearing this story of the two loving brothers. He visited the place where the brothers encountered one another in the field. And that is where he decided to build the Holy Temple of Jerusalem.

Windows and Mirrors

MANY YEARS AGO, a rich but miserly man visited his community's rabbi. They drank some tea quietly and looked out the window. "What do you see?" asked the rabbi. "Well, I see all kinds of people going about their business," answered the rich man.

The rabbi stood up and led his visitor to another room, which had a large mirror leaning against the wall. "And what do you see now?" he asked the rich man. "Now I see myself," the man replied impatiently. "Isn't it obvious?"

The rabbi patted his visitor on the shoulder. "Don't be mad," he requested softly. "But isn't this strange? Both the window and the mirror are made of glass. Yet, once you add a little silver to the glass and it becomes a mirror, you stop seeing others and are only able to see yourself."

A High Stage

RABBI JUDAH HANASI INSTALLED his learned protégé, the renowned Levi Bar Sissi, as the head judge and teacher of Simonia. The Simonians were overjoyed and quickly built a high platform in the center of town. They hauled Bar Sissi to the stage and gathered around.

Levi Bar Sissi was quite embarrassed by these high honors. He stood on stage, his feet trembling, as the people began to ask him questions about the Law of God. The first question was rather complex and Bar Sissi began to stutter. He could have sworn he knew the answer to the second question, but it simply escaped his mind. By the third question his head was completely blank. The questions kept on coming at Bar Sissi from all directions, and the poor Rabbi hunched speechless on the high stage. Before long, he climbed down from the platform and ran away from town.

Rabbi Judha HaNasi was surprised to see Levi Bar Sissi back in the old study hall. "What have the people of Simonia done to you?" he asked. "Why did they chase you away so quickly?"

Bar Sissi explained that all they did was ask him questions, but he was unable to provide proper answers. "But don't you know the answers to their questions?" asked the Rabbi. "Of course I do," replied Bar Sissi. "But standing on that high stage, I became so self-conscious I lost my head."

Rabbi Judah HaNasi nodded thoughtfully. "Now I understand," he mused out loud. "When a man is filled with high honors and pride, the Law of God escapes him."

Heaven of the Sages

AN ANONYMOUS RABBI DREAMT one night that he died and went to Heaven. In his dream, he asked the guards to take him to the area were the Jewish sages lived. The guards led him through marvelous fields and forests, until they finally reached a small synagogue. A few old rabbis were huddled around, engrossed in Bible study.

The rabbi was rather disappointed. "Is that all they do up in Heaven?!" he cried out. "And where are all the celebrated sages of all ages? Why are they not here?!"

The guards stared at the rabbi with blank expressions on their faces. They were accustomed to such mundane questions. "The sages are not here for a very simple reason," they explained. "It is because Heaven is within them!"

Three Wise Men

MANY YEARS AGO, a student asked Rabbi Menachem Mendel why Jews are not allowed to eat pork. "It doesn't really make any sense!" he said. "Also, it is a shame not to enjoy such delicious meat!" The Rabbi considered the question all evening. He opened his lecture the next day with a discussion of the Midrash:

"The Midrash speaks of three wise men," he said. "The first was able to reach a rare jewel that was hung on top of a high tree by joining together ladder upon ladder. The second was able to draw medicinal water from the depths of the earth by tying together rope upon rope. And the third gave people advice."

"One day, the third sage saw a group of workers arguing with their employer. The employer asked them to pour expensive wine into several barrels dotted with holes, and the workers were furious. 'This is just so unreasonable and futile!' they cried out. 'We don't want to do it!'"

"The wise man approached the workers and attempted to calm them down. 'As long as you are compensated,' he told them, 'does it really matter what the motives of your supervisor are?'"

Rabbi Menachem Mendel concluded his parable and observed his class. No one was talking. They all stared at their teacher waiting for an explanation.

"The third sage was obviously greater than the other two," he finally proclaimed, his voice thundering over the hall. "While the other two simply acted out of reason in order to reach their goal, the third acted out of faith! Therefore, the Biblical laws that seem to make little sense are in fact the most important! For we must follow them by faith in God's motives rather than by reason, and we shall be compensated!"

The Maze

ONCE UPON A TIME, an old king became weary of his numerous appointments and constant social engagements. Everyone seemed to have wanted a piece of him, and the king was exhausted. He decided to have his servants build a giant maze surrounding the palace in order to keep the stream of visitors away. And it worked. As soon as the construction was completed, the palace was quieter and calmer than it had ever been.

Yet, there were a few wise men who dared to enter the huge labyrinth. They advanced steadily within its twists and turns, pen and paper in hand, marking their way carefully. Slowly but surely, these studious men were eventually able to reach the secluded king.

Others, however, were not as sharp and composed. They yearned to see the illustrious king with all their hearts, and they simply ran into the maze frantically. Some gave up and escaped. Others got lost in the dreadful maze.

They wandered in it for years until they could not bear it any longer. They began to scream and cry for the king. And the old king took pity on them and came out to welcome them into his palace.

Those who truly longed for the king—both the sharp and the frantic—were eventually able to reach the palace. But which was the better path?

A Sincere Prayer

ONE COLD WINTER, Rabbi Sholom Schneersohn was bedridden with a terrible flu. His fever was awfully high, and no one knew whether the elderly teacher would be able to survive the disease. The entire community joined together in constant prayer for the well-being of their beloved Rabbi.

At the time, a solitary merchant arrived to town on business. He felt rather lonely in the unfamiliar city, and when evening came, he searched for a pub to have a drink, maybe two. But all the bars were closed. "Everyone is at the synagogue praying for Rabbi Schneersohn's health," he was informed.

The stranger did not know who Rabbi Schneersohn was. He returned to his hotel disappointed, his throat dry. He looked at the ceiling and prayed to God. "Please cure this ill Rabbi so I may have my drink!" he pleaded with all his heart.

That night, Rabbi Schneersohn started feeling a little better. His fever was completely gone by morning, and the Rabbi was back on his feet and at the synagogue after lunch. For God knows, no other prayer was as earnest as that of the lonely, thirsty stranger.

The Ugly Rabbi

THE BEAUTIFUL PRINCESS was sitting on her lovely verandah when she saw Rabbi Joshua Ben Hanania passing by on his way to see the king. "What an ugly person!" she blurted to no one in particular. "How could God produce such an unattractive creature?"

The Rabbi could not help but overhear the insolent comment. He smiled to himself and approached the princess. "Why does your father keep his refined wine in simple earth jars?" he asked her. "This is inappropriate for royalty like yourself. Why don't you move it to more suitable regal jars of silver and gold?"

The advice of the ugly Rabbi made much sense to the princess and she had her servants hurry and transfer the wine to beautiful jars of gold. But alas, within a few days, the refined wine turned sour.

The king was enraged when he heard that his wine was spoiled. He summoned the ugly Rabbi to the palace and asked him to explain his poor counsel to the princess. "I only did that in order to teach your daughter that wisdom should be kept in a plain container," explained the Rabbi.

"But is that really the case?" demanded the king. "Isn't wisdom sometimes contained in beautiful vessels?"

"Sure," agreed Rabbi Ben Hanania. "Wisdom can sometimes be found in good-looking bodies. But it would have been even greater if the body was ugly!"

The Mind-Reading Hassid

A DEVOUT HASSID packed his bags in preparation for the long journey to visit the Rabbi of Karlin. One of the local rabbis heard of this and invited the Hassid for tea. "Why must you travel so far to meet a rabbi?" he asked him. "We have plenty of rabbis around here."

"I am able to read the minds of all rabbis," boasted the Hassid. "And I can clearly see that all local rabbis are nothing but frauds!"

The local rabbi was offended and more than a little skeptical. "If you can truly read minds," he sneered, "why don't you tell me what I am thinking about right now!"

"Well, you are thinking of God, of course!" responded the Hassid.

"Wrong!" replied the rabbi. "I am not thinking of God. I suppose that proves you cannot read minds after all!"

"You may be right," answered the Hassid. "But that also proves that I must go visit the pious Rabbi of Karlin!"

The Wicked Lamb

A HORRIBLE PLAGUE spread through the forest. Animals were sick and dying. It must be a punishment from Heaven, assumed the poor creatures. We must try to stop it.

The king of the animals, the mighty lion, assembled all beasts to an emergency meeting. Tigers and wolves, snakes and reptiles, deer and sheep all arrived in a hurry. "Let us all confess our vices and root out the sinners who are responsible for this calamity!" roared the lion. "Otherwise, this epidemic will devour us all!"

The lion set an example by going first. He confessed the killing of a man who wandered into the forest alone. But the animals quickly dismissed his transgression. "You are the king of the forest!" they reasoned. "You must protect our territory from invaders. Surely, you did the right thing and God has forgiven you."

The wolf spoke next. In a low growl he confessed the killing and devouring of an innocent young calf. But again, the animals dismissed his transgression. "Hunger must have clouded your thinking," they reasoned. "Surely God has forgiven you."

One after another, the predators of the forest continued to confess their slaughters and carnages. But all were dismissed with various pretenses. Until it was time for the lamb to speak up and admit his sins.

"One day I was so hungry that I nibbled on the straw sandals of my herder," confessed the lamb. "Due to my sin, he had to walk barefoot for miles."

"How horrible!" roared the lion. "Absolutely cunning!" growled the wolf. "Thief! Criminal! Sinner! You brought this plague upon us!" the animals of the forest chanted in unison as they circled the wicked lamb, coming closer and closer. In no time, the beasts charged toward the lamb, and devoured him alive.

On One Foot

ONCE UPON A TIME, a non-Jewish gentleman fell in love with a pretty Jewish girl. He wanted to marry her right away, but she would not even consider it unless he converted.

Two wise rabbis lived in town at the time; Hillel and Shamai were their names. The love-struck gentleman rushed to Shamai's study hall first. "I must convert to Judaism immediately!" he told him. But Shamai just nodded his head sternly. "Conversion to Judaism is not a simple matter," he said. "It would take years of study and training."

The disappointed gentleman could not wait that long. After all, he was in love! He decided to give Rabbi Hillel a try. He ran to his house on the other side of town and asked him to convert him to Judaism. Hillel took a long look at the fervent gentleman and smiled. "No problem," he said.

"I can teach you the entire Law of God —
the thousands of pages of the Bible, the Talmud,
and the Mishna — while standing on one leg!"
said Hillel. He balanced on one foot and
continued. "All you have to know is this: What
is hateful to you, do not do to your fellow men!
This is the entire Law; the rest is just explanation.
Now hurry up and marry your loved one!"

List of Sources

48. Heaven of the Sages: *Pe'er VeKavod* by Rabbi Dov Ehrman.
49. Three Wise Men: *Fun Unzer Alten Otsar*.
50. The Maze: *Simchat Israel* by Rabbi Israel Berger.
51. A Sincere Prayer: *Siach Sarfei Kodesh*.
52. The Ugly Rabbi: *Babylonian Talmud, Masechet Ta'anit*.
53. The Mind-Reading Hassid: *Otsrot Idisher Humor*.
54. The Wicked Lamb: *Mishlei HaMagid me-Duvna*.
55. On One Foot: *Babylonian Talmud, Masechet Shabat*.

References for Further Reading

Glitsenstein, Avraham Chanoch. *Otzar Sipurey Chabad: An Anthology of Chabad Stories*. Israel: Kehot Publications, 1993.

Horen, Roee (ed.). *HaBa'al Shem Tov: HaIsh SheBah min HaYa'ar*. Rishon LeZion: Yedioth Ahronoth Books, 2017.

Kosman, Admiel. *Masechet Gvarim: Rav VeHaKatsav Ve'od Sipurim*. Jerusalem: Keter, 2002.

Lipsker, Avidav (ed.). *Encyclopedia shel HaSipur HaYehudi*. Ramat Gan: Bar Ilan University Press, 2017.

Lipson, Mordechai. *Emshol Lecha Meshal: Mishlei HaMagid me-Duvna*. New York: Dorot, 1956.

Neugroschel, Joachim. *No Star Too Beautiful: An Anthology of Yiddish Stories 1382 to the Present*. New York: W.W. Norton & Co Inc., 2002.

Newman, Louis (ed.). *Hasidic Anthology: Tales and Teachings of the Hasidim*. New York: Schoken Books, 1968.

Newman, Louis (ed.). *The Talmudic Anthology: Tales and Teachings of the Rabbis*. New York: Behrman House Inc., 1966.

Sahula, Isaac ben Solomon. *Meshal Haqadmoni: Fables from the Distant Past*. Edited and translated by Raphael Loewe. Portland, OR: The Littman Library of Jewish Civilization, 2004.

Schwartz, Howard. *A Palace of Pearls: The Stories of Rabbi Nachman of Bratslav*. New York: Oxford University Press, 2018.

WHAT DID YOU THINK OF

WISE TALES FROM THE JEWISH WORLD?

We hope that this book added meaning and quality to your life. If so, please share it with family, friends, and anyone else who may benefit from it.

Please feel free to add a review online or share your thoughts with us directly at prapanca_press@protonmail.com. Your feedback and support are valuable to us.

Thank you!

Made in the USA
Las Vegas, NV
27 March 2021